MAKING THE GRADE • GR

EASY POPULAR PIECES FOR YOUNG PIANISTS, SELECTED AND ARRANGED BY JERRY LANNING

Published by
Chester Music
14-15 Berners Street, London W1T 3LJ, England.

Exclusive Distributors:
Music Sales Limited
Distribution Centre, Newmarket Road, Bury St. Edmunds, Suffolk IP33 3YB, England.
Music Sales Pty Limited
120 Rothschild Avenue, Rosebery, NSW 2018, Australia.

Order No. CH67078
ISBN 1-84449-131-5

Music arranged by Jerry Lanning.
Music Processed by Camden Music.
Edited by Christopher Hussey.
Printed in the United Kingdom by Caligraving Limited, Thetford, Norfolk.

www.musicsales.com

Chester Music
part of The Music Sales Group

London / New York / Paris / Sydney / Copenhagen / Berlin / Madrid / Tokyo

INTRODUCTION

This revised and updated collection of 18 popular tunes provides additional attractive teaching repertoire to complement the first books in the MAKING THE GRADE series. As with previous books, the pieces have been carefully arranged and graded and the collection is made up of well-known material which pupils will enjoy.

The standard of pieces progresses to Associated Board Grade 2.

CONTENTS

JEAN DE FLORETTE (THEME)

Music by Jean-Claude Petit

Play the left hand very softly so that the tune stands out clearly.

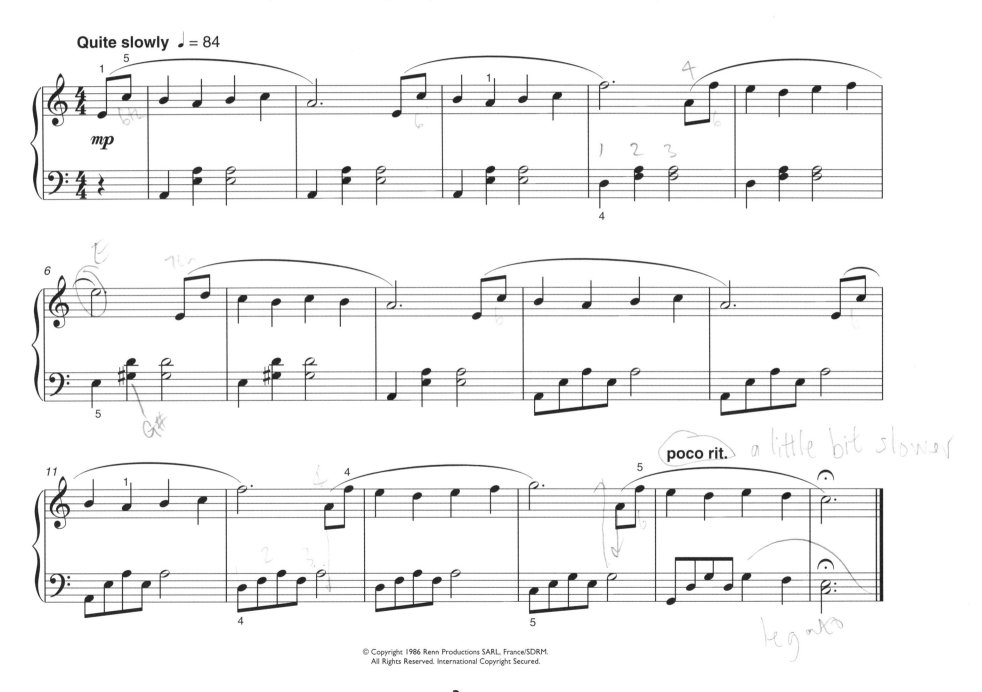

I HAVE A DREAM

Words & Music by Benny Andersson & Bjorn Ulvaeus

The left hand should be played *legato* throughout.

BEAUTY AND THE BEAST

Words by Howard Ashman
Music by Alan Menken

Notice how the left hand 'answers' the right hand when there are rests in the melody.

GET BACK

Words & Music by John Lennon & Paul McCartney

Don't let the left hand get too heavy and 'thump'.

MY HEART WILL GO ON

(Love Theme From 'Titanic')

Words by Will Jennings
Music by James Horner

Make sure that all the notes in each chord sound exactly together.

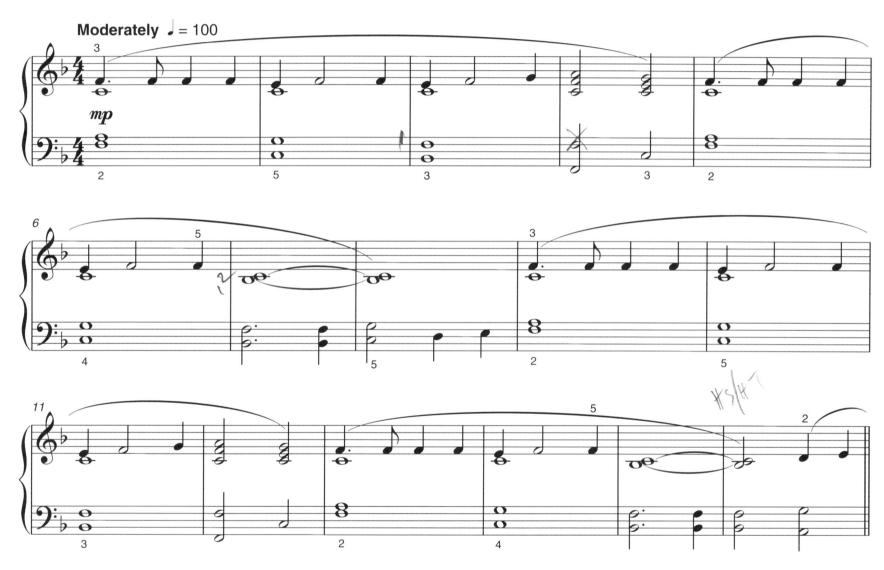

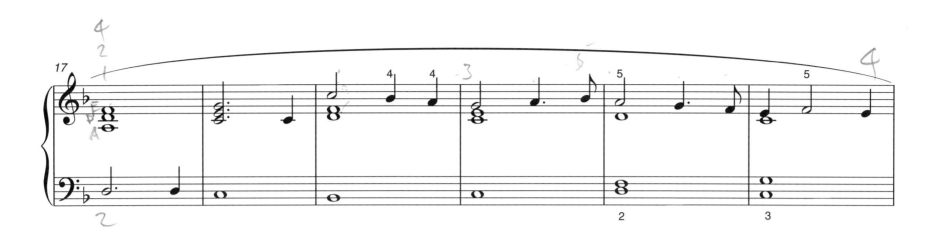

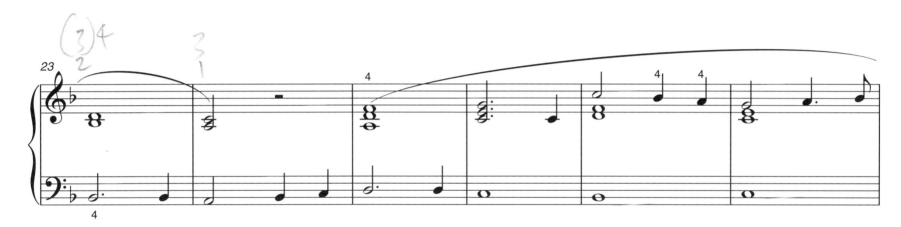

rall.

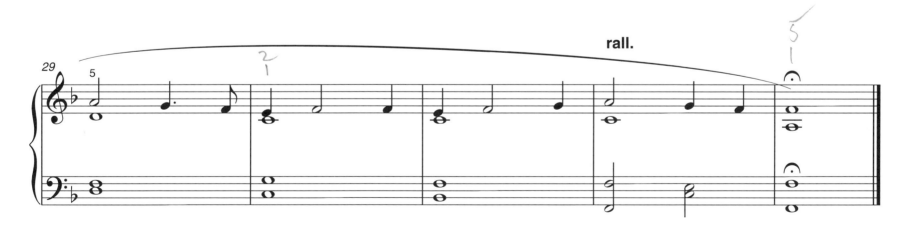

rallentando – slow down

MOON RIVER

Words by Johnny Mercer
Music by Henry Mancini

This song, featured in the film 'Breakfast At Tiffany's', needs smooth, gentle playing.

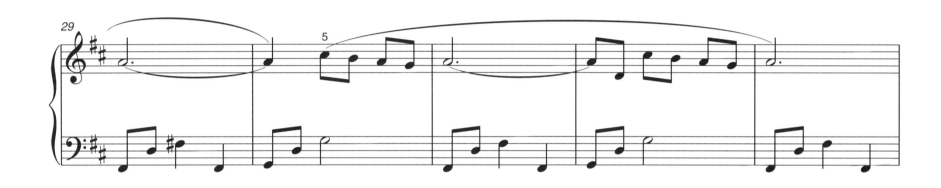

CLOCKS

Words & Music by Guy Berryman, Chris Martin, Jon Buckland & Will Champion

Keep the left hand quavers very steady and even.

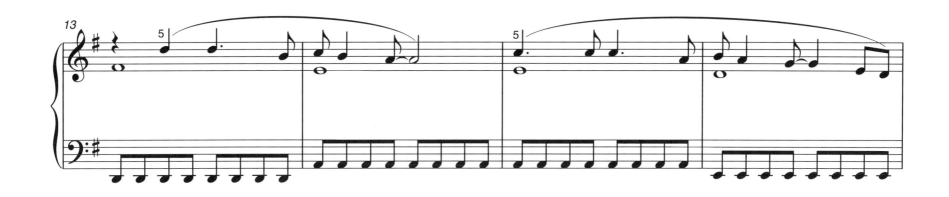

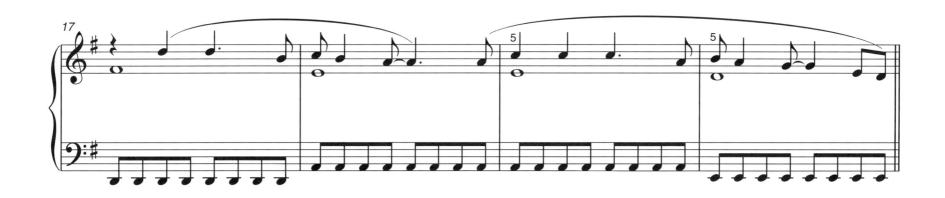

BRING ME SUNSHINE

Words by Sylvia Dee
Music by Arthur Kent

Keep the left hand light and bouncy. Practise the right hand fingering at bars 8–9 and 12–13 carefully.

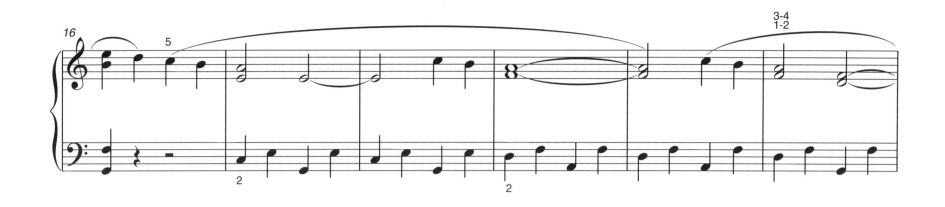

MR. TAMBOURINE MAN

Words & Music by Bob Dylan

Pay attention to the fingering and try to make the right hand as *legato* as possible.

AULD LANG SYNE

Traditional
Words by Robert Burns

Be careful with the right hand fingering and try to play as *legato* as possible.

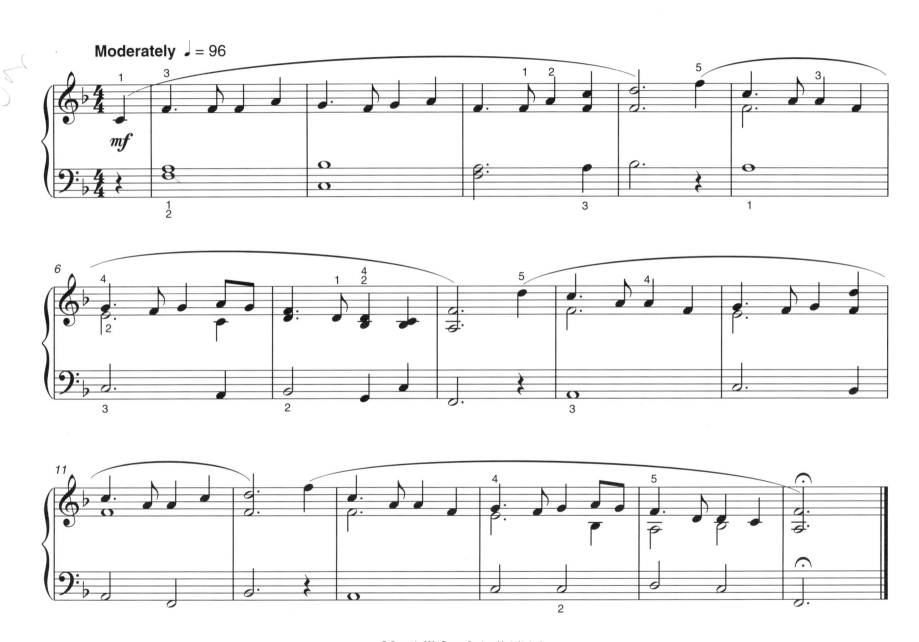

IF MY FRIENDS COULD SEE ME NOW

Words by Dorothy Fields
Music by Cy Coleman

Be sure to play the first three bars exactly in time.

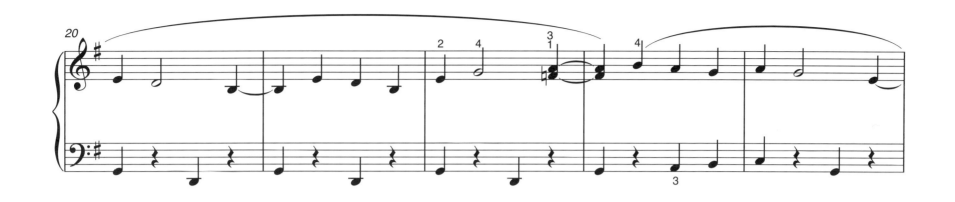

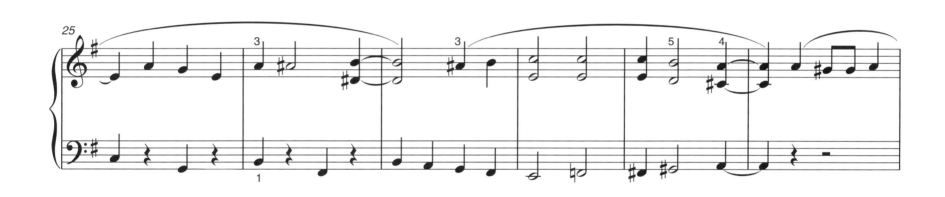

PENNIES FROM HEAVEN

Words by Johnny Burke
Music by Arthur Johnston

Make sure that the triplet crotchets in bar 29 are of equal length.

DIAMONDS ARE A GIRL'S BEST FRIEND

Words by Leo Robin
Music by Jule Styne

The right hand should be as *legato* as possible, except of course for the *staccato* chords.

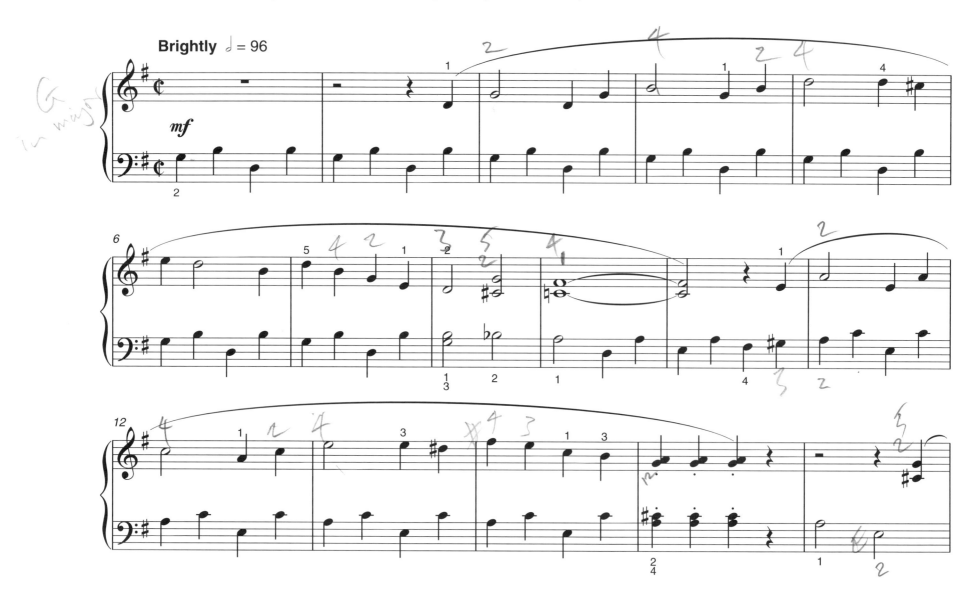

HOMEWARD BOUND

Words & Music by Paul Simon

There are a lot of repeated notes in the melody. Avoid playing them *staccato*, and imagine how you would sing them.

DON'T THINK TWICE, IT'S ALL RIGHT

Words & Music by Bob Dylan

Make sure you can read the treble stave notes in bars 5–8 before you start to practise this piece.

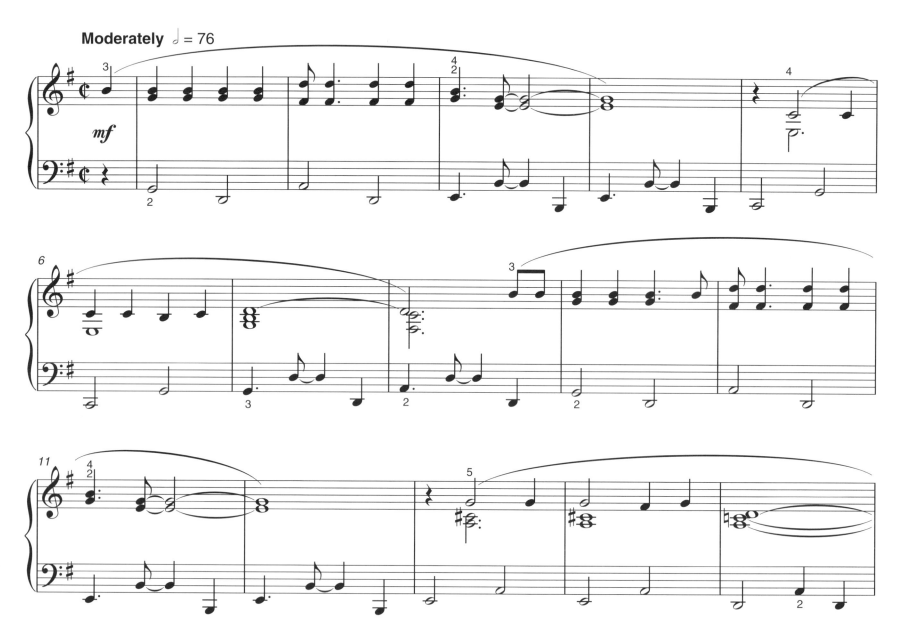

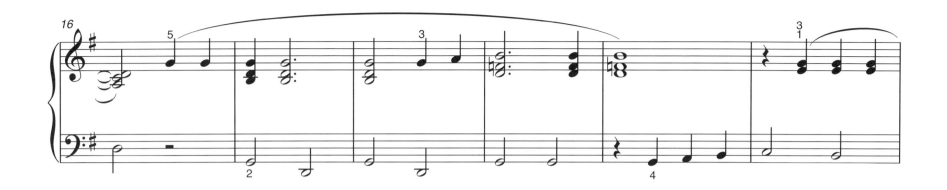

EMPTY CHAIRS AT EMPTY TABLES

(from 'Les Misérables')

Words by Alain Boublil & Herbert Kretzmer
Music by Claude-Michel Schönberg

Keep the left hand soft and be sure to hold on to the semibreves.

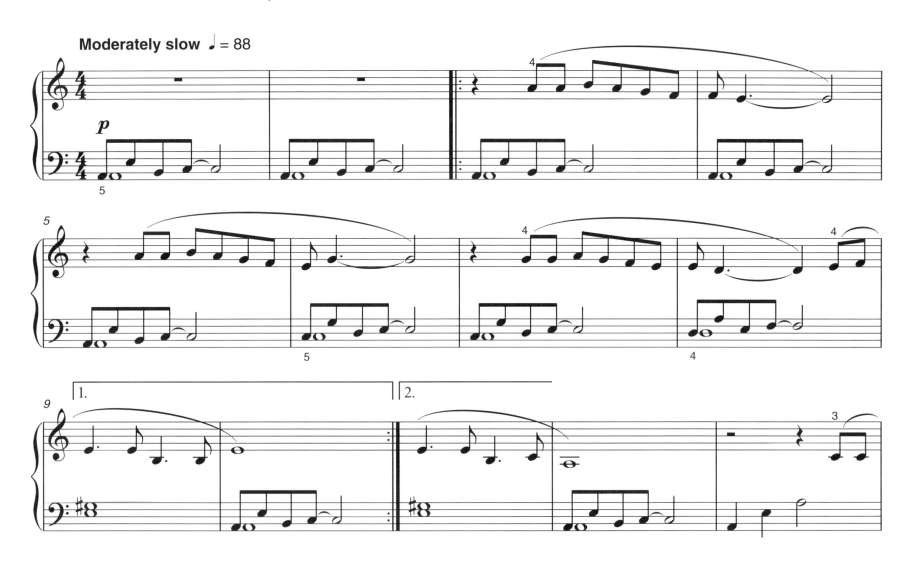

SHE'S THE ONE

Words & Music by Karl Wallinger

Keep the left hand crotchet chords steady, and play them quite lightly.

Moderately slow ♩ = 78

RAIDERS MARCH

(from 'Raiders Of The Lost Ark')

Music by John Williams

This is the theme from the film 'Raiders Of The Lost Ark'. It needs to be very rhythmic.

9/09(171111)